KOYOHARU GOTOUGE

They're publishing a graphic novel by me! Thank you! And heartfelt thanks to all the readers, my editors over the years, my assistants, everyone in the *Jump* editorial department, everyone at the printer, the people who designed the book, and the many other people who have offered their help!

DEMON SLAYER: KIMETSU NO YAIBA VOLUME 1
Shonen Jump Edition

Story and Art by
KOYOHARU GOTOUGE

KIMETSU NO YAIBA
© 2016 by Koyoharu Gotouge
All rights reserved. First published in Japan
in 2016 by SHUEISHA Inc., Tokyo. English
translation rights arranged by SHUEISHA Inc.

TRANSLATION John Werry
ENGLISH ADAPTATION Stan!
TOUCH-UP ART & LETTERING John Hunt
DESIGN Adam Grano
EDITOR Mike Montesa

The stories, characters and incidents mentioned
in this publication are entirely fictional.

Printed in Italy

Published by VIZ Media, LLC
P.O. Box 77010
San Francisco, CA 94107

33
First printing, July 2018
Thirty-third printing, July 2024

viz.com

CRUELTY

DEMON SLAYER

KIMETSU NO YAIBA

KOYOHARU GOTOUGE

CONTENTS

CRUELTY

HOW DID THIS HAPPEN?

CHAPTER 1: CRUELTY

YOUR BIG BROTHER IS DEFINITELY GOING TO SAVE YOU!

NEZUKO...

DON'T DIE.

DON'T DIE.

YOU CAN'T DIE.

I'M GONNA SAVE YOU.

CHAPTER 1: CRUELTY

TANJIRO!

YOU DON'T HAVE TO GO.

IT'S SNOWING AND IT'S DANGEROUS.

YOUR FACE IS PITCH-BLACK.

COME HERE.

THANK YOU.

...EVEN IF IT'S JUST A LITTLE.

I WANT US TO HAVE A GREAT NEW YEAR'S FEAST, SO I'LL GO SELL AS MUCH CHARCOAL AS I CAN...

WHAAAAA?! I WANNA GO TOO! TANJIRO, ARE YOU GOING TO TOWN AGAIN TODAY?

...SO HE CAN'T PULL YOU WHEN YOU'RE TIRED.

HE ISN'T TAKING THE CART TODAY...

BUT MOM!

NO.

NO. YOU CAN'T WALK FAST LIKE TANJIRO.

...I WAS HOPING WE'D DO IT TOGETHER.

I WILL, BUT...

I wanna go with you!

TAKEO...

I KNOW YOU CAN'T DO A LOT, BUT CUT A LITTLE WOOD TODAY. OKAY?

BE CAREFUL!

HURRY BACK, OKAY?

I WAS PUTTING ROKUTA TO SLEEP...

NEZUKO...

...BUT I HEARD ALL THE COMMOTION.

TANJIRO!

SEE YOU LATER!

...SO THEY'VE STARTED CLINGING TO YOU.

THEY'VE BEEN SO LONELY SINCE FATHER DIED...

IT'S ALWAYS CHANG-ING.

BUT LIFE IS LIKE THE WEATHER...

OUR LIFE ISN'T EASY, BUT WE'RE HAPPY.

...AND THE SNOW WON'T ALWAYS KEEP FALLING.

IT WON'T ALWAYS BE EASY...

...THE SMELL OF BLOOD IN THE AIR.

WHEN HAPPI-NESS ENDS THERE'S ALWAYS...

OH, TANJIRO!

THANKS FOR FIXING MY SHOJI DOOR THE OTHER DAY!

YOU'LL CATCH A COLD!

YOU CAME DOWN THE MOUNTAIN ON A DAY LIKE TODAY? YOU WORK SO HARD!

GIVE ME SOME CHARCOAL TOO!

HEY! SELL ME SOME CHARCOAL!

HELP ME!

SHE SAYS I BROKE A DISH!

SMELL IT!

YOU'RE JUST IN TIME!

AAAH! TANJIRO!

SNIFF

SNIFF
SNIFF

WILL YOU HELP ME CARRY SOME BUNDLES?!

TANJIRO!

I TOLD YOU IT WASN'T ME!

A CAT? OH DEAR.

I SMELL A CAT.

SEEEE?!

WHEW! IT'S GETTING LATE!

TP TP TP TP

IT'S TOO DANGER-OUS!

HEY, TANJIRO! YOU AREN'T...

...GOING BACK UP THE MOUNTAIN ARE YOU?!

14

BUT...

IT'S ALL RIGHT. YOU'RE WELCOME HERE.

YOU CAN STAY HERE.

COME BACK.

PLEASE.

I'VE GOT A GOOD NOSE FOR TROUBLE. I'LL BE FINE.

YOU DON'T WANT TO RUN INTO ANY *DEMONS*.

SO YOU SHOULDN'T WALK AROUND AT NIGHT.

EAT, THEN SLEEP. YOU CAN GET UP AND GO HOME EARLY TOMORROW.

FOR AGES...

... MAN-EATING DEMONS HAVE ROAMED THESE WOODS AFTER DARK.

YES...

...THEY CAN.

CAN'T THE DEMONS COME INSIDE HOUSES?

BUT...

BECAUSE *DEMON SLAYERS* CUT THEM DOWN.

HAVE FOR AGES...

...WHY DON'T THEY EAT EVERY-ONE?

... THEN ...

BUT...

YAWN

YAWN

THERE'S NO NEED TO FEAR. THERE'S NO SUCH THING AS DEMONS.

NEXT TIME, I'LL BRING MY LITTLE BROTHERS.

OLD MAN SABURO LIVES ALONE BECAUSE HE LOST HIS FAMILY. HE MUST BE LONELY.

BUT NOW THAT I THINK OF IT...

...MY GRANDMOTHER SAID THE SAME THING BEFORE SHE DIED.

WHEN HAPPI-NESS ENDS THERE'S ALWAYS...

...THE SMELL OF BLOOD IN THE AIR.

HFF

HFF

WHAT HAP—

WHAT HAPPENED?!

AGH!

WHAT THE...?

NEZUKO
...

ROKUTA
...

TAKEO...

SHIGERU
...

MOTHER
...

HANAKO
...

MAYBE A DOCTOR CAN SAVE HER.

ONLY NEZUKO'S BODY WAS STILL WARM.

MAYBE A BEAR TOO HUNGRY TO HIBERNATE?

HOW DID THIS HAPPEN? A BEAR?

KEEP GOING!

MOVE YOUR FEET FASTER.

THE AIR'S SO COLD IT'S FREEZING MY LUNGS.

SO HARD TO BREATHE!

I HAVE TO SAVE YOU.

TWITCH

I WON'T LET YOU DIE.

IT'S STILL A LONG WAY TO TOWN.

YOUR BIG BROTHER WILL SAVE YOU!

SH WF

?!

WHmP

I'M SLIP—

OH NO!

BUT IT ALSO MADE ME SLIP!

THE SNOW...

...SAVED ME.

NEZUKO!

!!

...CARRY YOU INTO TOWN!

YOU SHOULDN'T BE UP!

LET ME...

NEZUKO!

ARE YOU ALL RIGHT?

SHF

NEZUKO ...

WHMP

OMP

CH

I THOUGHT OF WHAT OLD MAN SABURO SAID.

A DEMON!

WAS NEZUKO...

...A MAN-EATING DEMON?

NEZUKO HAS BEEN HUMAN...

...SINCE THE DAY SHE WAS BORN.

NO, THAT WAS IM-POSSIBLE.

...FALLEN OVER ROKUTA, LIKE SHE WAS PROTECTING HIM.

BUT NEZUKO COULDN'T HAVE DONE ALL THAT. I FOUND HER...

BUT THIS NEZUKO...

...SMELLS OF BLOOD AND DEATH.

WHOOMP

SHE DIDN'T HAVE ANY BLOOD ON HER MOUTH OR HANDS.

AND THERE'S YET...

SKRR

...AN-OTHER SMELL...

SHFF

SKRK

26

...AND SHE'S GETTING STRONGER!

...SHE'S GROWING BIGGER...

WHAT-EVER THE REASON...

...HAPPENED TO MY WHOLE FAMILY!

WHILE I WAS SAFELY ASLEEP IN TOWN, SOMETHING HORRIBLE...

BUT SHE'S SO STRONG! I CAN'T PUSH HER AWAY!

NEZUKO!

I HAVE TO SAVE NEZUKO IF I CAN!

HOW THEY MUST HAVE SUFFERED.

...AND I WASN'T THERE TO HELP THEM.

BE STRONG!

YOU CAN DO IT!

DON'T TURN INTO A DEMON!

FIGHT IT! FIGHT FOR YOUR LIFE!

HOLD ON, NEZUKO!

PL IP

PL IP

PL IP

NEZUKO!

SNAP

WHO...

FMP

WHO IS THAT?

A
KATANA...

WHY
DO YOU
PROTECT
HER?

GRAAR

S-SISTER...

SHE'S MY...

...LITTLE SISTER!

THAT IS YOUR LITTLE SISTER?

RAAGH

GRAAH

SNATCH

DASH

...

NEZUKO!

HW SH!

DON'T MOVE.

WAIT! NEZUKO HASN'T KILLED ANYONE!

SO OF COURSE, I'LL TAKE YOUR LITTLE SISTER'S HEAD TOO.

KILLING DEMONS IS MY JOB.

THAT MUST BE WHO KILLED EVERYONE!

...FROM SOMEONE I'VE NEVER SMELLED BEFORE!

THERE WAS A SCENT AT MY HOUSE...

THAT'S EASY. DEMON BLOOD GOT IN HER WOUND, SO SHE'S TRANSFORMED INTO A DEMON.

GRAAR!

NOT NEZUKO!

BUT...

I DON'T KNOW WHAT'S MAKING HER ACT LIKE THIS...

THAT IS HOW MAN-EATING DEMONS MULTIPLY.

NO! I'M SURE SHE KNOWS WHO I AM!

A MOMENT AGO SHE ALMOST ATE *YOU!*

NEZUKO WOULD NEVER EAT ANYONE!

I'LL MAKE HER *HUMAN* AGAIN!

I'LL FIND A WAY TO *CURE* HER!

I *WON'T* LET HER HURT ANYONE!

I'LL FIND A WAY! I SWEAR! PLEASE DON'T KILL HER!

A HUMAN WHO BECOMES A DEMON CANNOT GO BACK.

SHE WON'T GET BETTER.

SH NN NG

...SO...

...SO...

I'LL ALSO FIND THE ONE THAT KILLED MY FAMILY!

I'LL DO ALL THAT, SO...

I CAN'T LOSE NEZUKO TOO!

STOP!

PLEASE...

PLEASE, STOP.

PLEASE DON'T KILL MY LITTLE SISTER!

PLEASE...

NEVER LEAVE YOURSELF SO *DEFENSELESS* IN FRONT OF AN ENEMY!

STOP BOWING SO PITIFULLY!

IF THAT WORKED, YOUR FAMILY WOULD STILL BE ALIVE!

FLINCH

...CURE HIS LITTLE SISTER?

OR EVEN *FIND* HIS ENEMY?

HOW CAN A WEAKLING LIKE YOU, WHO BOWS DOWN WHEN IT'S TIME TO FIGHT, TO KILL OR BE KILLED... HOW CAN SUCH A MAN...

...YOU MUST FIGHT FOR IT!

IF YOU WANT SOME-THING...

DEMONS MIGHT KNOW HOW TO CURE YOUR LITTLE SISTER...

...NO DEMON WILL RESPECT YOUR WHINING AND BEGGING!

...BUT...

THE MEEK HAVE NO POWER AND NO OPTIONS!

THE STRONG WILL CRUSH THEM IN EVERY WAY!

YOUR HEART IS CRUSHED.

YOUR FAMILY IS DEAD AND YOUR SISTER HAS BECOME A DEMON.

I KNOW YOUR PAIN, HOW YOU MUST WANT TO CRY OUT.

DON'T CRY.

DON'T DESPAIR.

THOSE THINGS WILL DO YOU NO GOOD.

BUT THERE IS NO TURNING BACK TIME.

...YOUR FAMILY MIGHT HAVE SURVIVED.

IF I'D COME HALF A DAY SOONER ...

ANGER THAT BECOMES THE UNWAVERING FORCE THAT DRIVES YOUR LIMBS.

...THAT GIVES NO QUARTER.

STRONG, PURE ANGER...

FILL YOUR HEART WITH ANGER.

...CANNOT PROTECT YOUR SISTER OR FIND HER A CURE.

WEAKNESS AND EMPTY PROMISES...

AND THEY CERTAINLY CANNOT AVENGE YOUR FAMILY.

W...

SH—NK

GUFFH!

AAAAH!

WIHOK

WHAT A FOOL!

A SIMPLE, HEAD-ON ATTACK RELYING ON PURE EMOTION.

JUST BEFORE PASSING BEHIND THE TREE, HE THREW A ROCK...

...AND WHILE HIDDEN BY THE TREE HE THREW HIS HATCHET.

...WAS TO STRIKE ME DOWN AFTER I KILLED HIM.

HE KNEW HE COULDN'T WIN AGAINST ME, SO HIS PLAN...

HE HID HIS HAND SO I WOULDN'T SEE HE WAS UNARMED.

GRAAR!

THIS KID...

WHOK

NO! I'M TOO LATE!

SKF

SHE'S ABOUT TO EAT HIM!

NEZUKO...

NEZUKO WOULD NEVER EAT ANYONE!

NOT NEZUKO!

HE WOULDN'T BE...

...THE FIRST TO SAY THAT AND THEN GET EATEN ANYWAY.

BECAUSE THEY NEED THE ENERGY.

STARVING DEMONS WILL KILL AND EAT THEIR OWN PARENTS AND SIBLINGS.

I'VE SEEN IT COUNTLESS TIMES.

...AND MUST WANT TO EAT HUMAN FLESH AS SOON AS POSSIBLE.

...NOT TO MENTION THE STRENGTH IT TOOK TO TRANSFORM INTO A DEMON. SHE MUST BE DOUBLY STARVED RIGHT NOW...

THIS GIRL IS INJURED. IT COSTS HER STRENGTH...

...TO HEAL THAT WOUND...

...AND FOCUSING HER ANGER ON ME.

BUT SHE'S PROTECTING HIM...

I'M SORRY I HAD TO LEAVE YOU, TANJIRO.

TAKE CARE OF NEZUKO.

HWSH

HMMPH

YOU'RE AWAKE?

TELL HIM THAT *GIYU TOMIOKA* SENT YOU.

GO SEE AN OLD MAN NAMED *SAKONJI UROKODAKI* WHO LIVES AT THE FOOT OF MOUNT SAGIRI.

WHSH

...BUT DON'T LET HER INTO DIRECT SUNLIGHT.

YOUR SISTER SHOULD BE FINE BECAUSE THE SUN ISN'T OUT TODAY...

STARE

CHAPTER 2: THE STRANGER

...AND A LITTLE STRAW AND BAMBOO?

...BUT MAY I TAKE THAT BASKET...

I BEG YOUR PARDON...

THAT'S ALL RIGHT. CAN I PAY YOU?

NO NEED. IT'S A BROKEN BASKET.

...BUT THE BASKET HAS A HOLE IN IT.

WE DON'T MIND...

WE DON'T WANT IT!

BUT I *WANT* TO PAY!

WHAT A STUBBORN KID!

NO, THANK YOU.

SHAKE SHAKE

PLEASE LET ME PAY.

YOU CAN HAVE THE OTHER STUFF TOO.

JUST TAKE IT! IT'S ONLY A FEW COINS ANYWAY!

OWWW!

THANK YOU VERY MUCH!

SHE'S GONE!

HMM?

NEZUKO...

NEZUKO!

...

POP

THERE SHE IS!

JUST WAIT.

SHE MUST REALLY NOT WANT THE SUNLIGHT TO HIT HER.

HER FACE IS SCRUNCHED UP.

MY SISTER IS LIKE A MOLE NOW.

DID SHE DIG THAT HOLE?

TA-DAH!

FWIK

FWIK

FWIK

...

GET IN.

HERE.

THE BASKET.

I WANT US TO TRAVEL DURING THE DAY.

I'LL CARRY YOU.

WILL YOU FIT IN HERE?

NEZUKO HAS GROWN UP.

I STILL THINK SHE'S A LITTLE GIRL.

YOU'RE TOO BIG.

...RE- VERSE THAT...

...AND GET SMALLER?

NEZUKO...

...YOU'RE AS BIG AS AN ADULT. CAN YOU...

HMM?

STUFF

AH!

GET SMALLER!

NEZUKO.

SMALLER.

FLOP

FLOP

FWUP

YEOW!

OH! GOOD!

KAW
KAW

GOOD GIRL, NEZUKO!

PAT PAT

THAT'S PERFECT!

I'M IMPRESSED!

THE SUN WILL SET SOON.

AND YOU'RE GOING TO CARRY THAT HUGE LOAD? IT'S DANGEROUS.

TO GET TO MOUNT SAGIRI, YOU FIRST HAVE TO CROSS THAT MOUNTAIN.

...SO DON'T GET LOST!

PEOPLE REALLY DO DISAPPEAR UP THERE...

THANK YOU VERY MUCH.

BOW

I'LL BE PLENTY CAREFUL.

OH!

!!

I SMELL BLOOD!

THERE'S A WAY STATION.

THERE'S A LIGHT ON. SOMEONE MUST BE THERE.

LET'S GO.

ARE YOU ALL RIGHT?

THESE MOUNTAIN PATHS ARE DANGEROUS. THAT TRAVELER MAY BE INJURED!

KLAK

KT K

HMM...?

SOMETHING'S WRONG HERE.

DLP
DLP
DLP

A MAN-EATING DEMON!

ARE YOU TWO HUMAN?

HRF HRF

SH-SHE JUST KILLED HIM! WELL, HE WAS A DEMON, SO...

KO NK

WHY YOUUU ...!

I CAN'T BELIEVE IT! IT JUST MOVED WITH ITS HEAD RIPPED OFF!

WHAT ARE A DEMON AND A HUMAN DOING TOGETHER?!

I KNEW IT! ONE OF YOU IS A DEMON!

SOMETHING DIDN'T SEEM RIGHT!

TMP TMP TMP

IT'S STILL TALK-ING!!

STOP!

MY HAIR IS TANGLED UP ON THE HAFT! AND I GREW THESE HANDS TOO SHORT, SO I CAN'T GET A GRIP!

ARGH!!

HE PINNED ME TO THE TREE WITH HIS HATCHET!

NEZUKO!

WHSH

GYAAAH!

SPLAT

WOW!

HOW MANY DEMONS ARE THERE?

SHNG

SO I HAVE TO DO THIS.

HFF HFF HFF HFF

BUT...

...IF I DON'T KILL HIM, HE'LL ATTACK MORE PEOPLE.

A DIFFERENT DEMON.

HE SMELLS DIFFERENT THAN THE ONE THAT WAS AT MY HOUSE.

DO IT!

CHAPTER 3: RETURN BY DAWN

...LORD SAKONJI UROKODAKI.

GREETINGS...

A DEMON SLAUGHTERED HIS FAMILY...

HE HAD THE COURAGE TO FIGHT ME UNARMED.

I HAVE SENT A BOY YOUR WAY WHO SAYS HE WANTS TO BECOME A DEMON-SLAYING SWORDSMAN.

...BUT SHE CHOOSES NOT TO ATTACK HUMANS.

...TRANSFORMING HIS SURVIVING SISTER INTO A DEMON...

I BELIEVE THAT PERHAPS...

I SENSE SOMETHING IN THESE TWO THAT IS DIFFERENT FROM THE OTHERS.

LIKE YOU, THE BOY HAS A STRONG SENSE OF SMELL.

I KNOW THIS IS A SELFISH REQUEST, SO PLEASE FORGIVE ME.

...HE COULD BE WORTHY OF CARRYING ON YOUR TRADITIONS.

PLEASE, TRAIN HIM.

SIN-CERELY...

...GIYU TOMIOKA.

...AND IN GOOD SPIRITS.

MAY THIS FIND YOU IN GOOD HEALTH...

DON'T TRUST WHAT OTHERS SAY.

CAN'T YOU SOLVE THIS RIDDLE YOURSELF?

HE MOVED, IN COMPLETE SILENCE.

H...

HOW *CAN* I FINISH *IT* OFF?

A *TENGU* MASK!

I'LL HAVE TO CRUSH THE HEAD...

...

IF STAB-BING IT WON'T WORK...

NN GH

ISN'T THERE ANY WAY TO KILL IT WITH ONE BLOW?

TO COMPLETELY CRUSH THE HEAD, I'LL HAVE TO SMASH IT WITH A ROCK REPEATEDLY.

IT WILL SURELY SUFFER.

SNAFF

WHEN FACING A DEMON, HE STILL REEKS OF SYMPATHY AND CONSIDERATION.

HE EVEN FEELS SYMPATHY FOR A DEMON.

HIS KINDNESS PREVENTS HIM FROM TAKING DECISIVE ACTION.

DAMN...

...THIS KID IS NO GOOD.

I WAS UNCONSCIOUS.

I FEEL SICK.

IS MY BODY DEAD?

...THIS BOY IS USELESS.

GIYU...

WHA—?

...

JUST A TOUCH OF SUN-LIGHT DID THAT?!

NO WONDER NEZUKO FEARS IT!

OH, YEAH...

...THAT GUY.

UM...

HE'S BURYING THE DEMON'S VICTIMS.

Y...

YES.

I'M TANJIRO KAMADO.

MY SISTER IS NEZUKO.

I AM SAKONJI UROKODAKI.

YOU MUST BE THE ONE GIYU TOLD ME ABOUT.

...WHAT WILL YOU *DO* WHEN YOUR SISTER EATS SOMEONE?

TELL ME, TANJIRO...

YOU THINK *TOO* SLOWLY!

!!

WHY COULDN'T YOU ANSWER THAT QUESTION IMMEDIATELY?

...

YOU COULD NEVER FINISH OFF A DEMON BEFORE THE MORNING LIGHT.

YOU STRUGGLE OVER THE SIMPLEST DECISIONS.

YOU ARE TOO SOFT!

THAT IS WHAT IT MEANS TO TRAVEL WITH YOUR SISTER WHO HAS BECOME A DEMON!

WHEN YOUR SISTER EATS SOMEONE, THERE ARE TWO THINGS YOU HAVE TO DO...

KILL YOUR SISTER... THEN SLIT YOUR OWN BELLY AND DIE!

DO YOU UNDER-STAND WHAT I AM SAYING?

YOUR SISTER MUST NEVER TAKE THE LIFE...

...OF AN INNOCENT PERSON!

BUT IT IS YOUR SACRED DUTY TO ENSURE THAT THIS NEVER HAPPENS.

VERY WELL...

...I WILL TEST YOU TO SEE IF YOU HAVE WHAT IT TAKES...

...TO BE A DEMON-SLAYER SWORDS-MAN.

YES!

SHOULDER YOUR SISTER AND FOLLOW ME.

AND HIS FEET REALLY DON'T MAKE ANY SOUND!

HFF

HFF

HF

HE'S FAST!

HOW OLD IS THIS GUY?!

...SUFFERING IS ALL YOU'VE EVER KNOWN...

BUT THEN...

...LITTLE SISTER.

...THIS'LL BE ROUGH, BUT HANG IN THERE!

NEZUKO...

YOU SHOULD BUY A NEW ONE.

ARE YOU MENDING YOUR KIMONO AGAIN?

...TO GIVE THE YOUNGER KIDS PLENTY TO EAT.

INSTEAD, I USE THAT MONEY...

I LIKE THIS KIMONO!

NO, NO...

...I'M FINE.

EVERYTHING I COULDN'T GIVE TO THEM, I'LL GIVE TO YOU!

AND THEN I'LL BUY YOU A BEAUTIFUL KIMONO!

I WILL MAKE YOU HUMAN AGAIN!

THIS TIME, I WILL NOT WAIT UNTIL SUNRISE.

NOW YOU MUST DESCEND TO THE HOUSE AT THE FOOT OF THE MOUNTAIN.

HFF

HFF

OH, I GET IT.

HE THINKS I'LL GET LOST IN THIS THICK FOG.

IS THAT ALL?

HFF

HFF

GWEH

HUH?

THAT'S EASY! I HAVE A SHARP NOSE!

I'VE ALREADY MEMORIZED UROKODAKI'S SCENT.

I JUST HAVE TO GET BACK BEFORE SUNRISE.

HFF

HFF

HFF

I GET IT!

A COVERED PIT!

UH-OH! HERE WE GO AGAIN!

WSH

THESE ARE ALL TRAPS.

THAT'S THE CHALLENGE!

MMPH

THW OK

I'M IN BIG TROUBLE.

HFF

HFF

WHUD

AND I JUST NOTICED... UP ON THIS MOUNTAIN...

IF I KEEP SETTING OFF EVERY TRAP, I WON'T GET DOWN THE MOUNTAIN BY MORNING.

HFF

HFF

HFF

HFF

HFF

IT'S MUCH WORSE THAN THE MOUNTAIN WE LIVED ON!

...THE AIR'S SO THIN I CAN BARELY BREATHE!

CONTROL YOUR BREATHING. SNIFF OUT THE TRAPS.

I FEEL LIKE I MIGHT PASS OUT!

NO! I'VE GOTTA GET BACK!

THAT'S WHY I FEEL SO TIRED AND DIZZY.

YES! I CAN SMELL THEM!

TRAPS HAVE TO BE SET BY SOMEONE, AND THOSE SCENTS MUST LINGER.

...THE ABILITY TO EVADE THEM ALL!

BUT KNOWING THEY'RE THERE DOESN'T GRANT ME...

ZZZ

ZZZ

ZZZ

THUNK THUNK
KTNK

SHMP

SHMP

I...

...MADE
IT...

...BACK.

HFF

HFF

HFF

...I ACCEPT
YOU AS MY
STUDENT!

TANJIRO
KAMADO...

Taisho Whispers
& Rumors

○ 鬼滅奇譚 (Kimetsu Kitan) (Mysterious Story of the Demon Slayer)

○ 鬼鬼滅滅 (Kikimetsumetsu) (Demon Demon Slayer Slayer)

○ 悪鬼滅々 (Akkimetsumetsu) (Evil Demon Slayer)

○ 鬼殺の刃 (Kisatsu no Yaiba) (Sword of the Demon Killer)

○ 滅々鬼譚 (Metsumetsu Kitan) (Strange Tale of the Demon Slayer)

○ 鬼殺譚 (Kisatsutan) (Tale of the Demon Killer)

○ 空想鬼滅奇譚 (Kuso Kimetsu Kitan) (The Fantastic Strange Tale of the Demon Slayer)

○ 鬼狩リカグツチ (Onigari Kagutsuchi) (Demon Hunting God of Fire)

○ 炭のカグツチ (Sumi no Kagutsuchi) (Charred God of Fire)

* "Kitan" means an unusual and mysterious story.

* "Kagutsuchi" is a god of fire.

Hello, I'm Gotoge.

I hear these titles were under consideration.

Which one do you like?

THE DEMON SLAYER CORPS FIGHTS DEMONS FACE-TO-FACE.

THEY ARE HUMAN, SO THEIR WOUNDS HEAL, SLOWLY AND LOST-LIMBS DO NOT RETURN.

NONETHELESS, THEY FIGHT DEMONS IN ORDER TO PROTECT ORDINARY PEOPLE.

THERE ARE MANY TRAINERS. IN DIFFERENT PLACES, THEY USE VARIOUS TRAINING METHODS.

I AM A TRAINER.

JUST LIKE IT SOUNDS, I TRAIN SWORDSMEN.

I DECIDE WHETHER YOU MAY ATTEMPT FINAL SELECTION.

IN ORDER TO JOIN THE DEMON SLAYER CORPS, YOU MUST SURVIVE THE FINAL SELECTION AT MOUNT FUJIKASANE.

AGAIN TODAY, I DESCENDED THE MOUNTAIN.

STARTING TODAY, I HAVE DECIDED TO WRITE THIS JOURNAL FOR NEZUKO.

I TRAIN AS HARD AS I CAN SO I WON'T DIE DURING FINAL SELECTION.

I'M GROWING STRONGER ...

...AND MY NOSE IS EVEN SHARPER AT PICKING UP SCENTS.

I GO DOWN THE MOUNTAIN REPEATEDLY, DAY AFTER DAY. I'VE BECOME QUITE GOOD AT AVOIDING TRAPS.

IT'S LIKE HE REALLY WANTS TO KILL ME.

THOK THOK

BUT THE TRAPS ARE GETTING MUCH DEADLIER.

IT REALLY GETS IN THE WAY...

...SO CARRYING IT GOT ME CAUGHT IN A LOT OF TRAPS.

TODAY, I WENT DOWN THE MOUNTAIN WITH A KATANA.

AFTER DESCENDING THE MOUNTAIN, I SWING THE SWORD SO MUCH I FEEL LIKE MY ARMS MIGHT FALL OFF.

SWSH SWSH

I SAY "TODAY," BUT LATELY I DO THIS EVERY DAY.

TODAY, I PRACTICED SWINGING THE SWORD.

...715...

...716...

...713...

...714...

WITH A KATANA...

IT'S STRONG AGAINST FORCE LENGTHWISE BUT WEAK AGAINST FORCE FROM THE SIDE.

THE FIRST THING HE TAUGHT ME WAS THAT A KATANA BREAKS EASILY.

WHEN YOU SWING A KATANA...

...YOU MUST ATTACK STRAIGHT AHEAD.

...THE DIRECTION OF THE BLADE AND THE DIRECTION OF THE FORCE YOU APPLY MUST BE EXACTLY THE SAME.

...HE'LL BREAK MY BONES. HIS THREATS ARE COLD...

IN OTHER WORDS, IF I BREAK IT...

...YOU!

FURTHER-MORE...

...IF YOU DAMAGE THE SWORD, HE'LL DAMAGE...

...LIKE THE MOUNTAIN.

TODAY, I DID NOTHING BUT FALL DOWN...

...TRAINING TO BREAK MY FALL AND GET UP QUICKLY.

URO-KODAKI STANDS AGAINST ME...

...UN-ARMED.

I WIELD MY SWORD AND FACE UROKODAKI WITH THE INTENT TO STRIKE HIM DOWN.

HE EASILY THROWS ME TO THE GROUND.

HUUUH?!

BUT HE'S RIDICU-LOUSLY STRONG.

I'VE BEEN WRITING...

...FOR SIX MONTHS, NEZUKO, AND YOU STILL HAVEN'T WOKEN UP.

NO!

NO!

THIS?

THIS?

LIKE THIS?

NO!

TODAY, I LEARNED BREATHING AND SOME STANDARD FORMS.

HE SAID I DIDN'T HAVE ENOUGH STRENGTH IN MY CORE, THEN HE GOT ANGRY AND HIT MY STOMACH.

BAM

AAGH!

BAM

YET IT'S CLEARLY STRANGE FOR YOU TO KEEP SLEEPING LIKE THIS.

UROKODAKI IMMEDIATELY CALLED A DOCTOR TO LOOK AT YOU...

...BUT HE FOUND NOTHING WRONG.

AND ...

...THAT'S STILL HOW I FEEL EVERY NIGHT.

I THOUGHT I'D WAKE UP IN THE MORNING TO FIND YOU DEAD.

I WAS SCARED.

MANY TIMES I'VE THOUGHT THAT I WOULD DIE.

AND EVERY DAY I GO HIGHER ON THE MOUNTAIN FOR MY TRAINING, EACH PLACE MORE DANGEROUS AND WITH THINNER AIR.

I HAVE NOTHING MORE TO TEACH YOU.

...THAT WAS ALL HE SAID.

ABOUT A YEAR AFTER I ARRIVED AT MOUNT SAGIRI...

HZZ

HZZ

HFF

HUH?

...TAKE WHAT I HAVE TAUGHT YOU AND BRING IT TO THE NEXT LEVEL?

CAN YOU...

THE REST IS UP TO YOU.

CAN YOU SPLIT IT WITH A KATANA?

CAN THAT EVEN BE SPLIT?!

A BOULDER....?

I DON'T THINK I CAN.

THE BLADE WOULD BREAK.

UROKO-DAKI!!

UROKO-DAKI!!

WAIT! THIS...

STOMP

...HASN'T TAUGHT ME ANYTHING.

...UROKO-DAKI...

SINCE THAT DAY...

HOLDING MY BREATH, FLEXIBILITY, AND THE MOST BASIC THINGS TOO.

STILL...

I'M GLAD I WROTE EVERYTHING DOWN IN MY JOURNAL.

...EVERY DAY I PRACTICE WHAT I LEARNED FROM UROKO-DAKI.

I'M BEGINNING TO WORRY.

BUT EVEN AFTER HALF A YEAR I STILL CAN'T SPLIT THE BOULDER.

I HAVE TO DO MORE.

MORE!

I HAVEN'T HAD ENOUGH TRAINING.

IT ISN'T ENOUGH.

CHAPTER 5: TANJIRO'S JOURNAL, PART 2

WHAT ARE YOU DOING?

WHERE'D YOU COME FROM?!

!!

HOW LONG DO YOU PLAN TO HAVE YOUR BUTT STUCK IN THE MUD?

TAKE A STANCE!

DOING?

I'M TRAIN-ING.

NOW... ATTACK!

STOMP

...YOU HAVE A WOODEN SWORD AND I HAVE A REAL ONE!

BUT...

HA HA HA HA!

HA HA!

HA HA HA!

...

HA HA HA HA!

HA HA HA!

WA HA HA HA!

YOU THINK YOU CAN HURT ME?

HOW SWEET!

THANKS FOR WORRYING ABOUT ME!

WHAK KLAK

YOU CAN'T HURT ME! I'M STRONGER THAN YOU'LL EVER BE! I'VE ALREADY SPLIT A BOULDER!

REST YOUR POOR, SOFT HEART.

YOU'VE GAINED NOTHING. YOU HAVEN'T MASTERED ANYTHING!

YOU SPLIT A BOULDER?!

YOU JUST MEMORIZED IT AS A FACT...

BUT YOUR BODY DOESN'T *UNDER-STAND* ANYTHING!

TOTAL CONCEN-TRATION BREATHING!

CER-TAINLY NOT...

...THE BREATHING TECHNIQUE TAUGHT BY UROKODAKI!

HE KNOWS UROKODAKI!?! AND ABOUT THE BREATHING...

!!

THUD

HMM.

FWP.

I LEAVE
THE REST
TO YOU.

ARE YOU ALL RIGHT?

DID YOU SEE WHAT HAPPENED?

SH WF

THAT'S HOW I WANT TO BE TOO!

BUT IS THAT EVEN POSSIBLE?

CAN I DO IT...?

THAT WAS AN INCREDIBLE BLOW!

IT WAS TRULY BEAUTIFUL!

NOT A BIT OF UNNECESSARY MOTION!

UH... WHO ARE YOU?

SHE'S CUTE...

I'LL WATCH OVER YOU.

I'M SURE YOU CAN.

...AND TELLS ME THE GUY'S NAME IS SABITO.

SHE SAYS HER NAME IS MAKOMO...

SHE CORRECTS MY UNNECESSARY MOVEMENTS AND BAD HABITS.

MAKOMO POINTS OUT THE DEFECTS IN MY STYLE.

I ASK, BUT SHE NEVER TELLS ME.

WHERE DID SHE COME FROM?

WHY IS SHE DOING THIS FOR ME?

SHE OFTEN SAYS THOSE WORDS.

WE REALLY LIKE URO-KODAKI.

THERE ARE OTHER CHILDREN TOO.

THEY'RE ALL AROUND, WATCHING YOU.

THEY AREN'T SIBLINGS. THEY WERE BOTH ORPHANS.

UROKO-DAKI TOOK THEM IN AND RAISED THEM.

TOTAL CONCEN-TRATION BREATH-ING...

...ACCELERATES YOUR BLOOD FLOW AND HEARTBEAT.

AND YOUR TEMPERATURE SHOOTS UP.

MAKOMO IS A BIT OF A STRANGE GIRL.

SHE SAYS THINGS IN A WEIRD WAY.

...AND BRING...

...LOTS OF AIR INTO YOUR BLOOD.

YOU EXPAND YOUR LUNGS...

YOU'RE STILL HUMAN, BUT YOU GET STRONG LIKE A DEMON.

YOU GET HOT AND STRONG!

YOUR BLOOD GETS EXCITED AND YOUR BONES AND MUSCLES THRILL.

HOW CAN THAT BE?

I DON'T REALLY GET IT...

BASICALLY, I DON'T THINK THERE'S ANY-THING ELSE YOU CAN DO.

YOU MUST TRAIN SO HARD THAT YOU COULD DIE.

...BUT... ...AND HEART WOULD BURST IN MY CHEST... ...MY LUNGS... ...AND THAT... ...IT FELT LIKE MY ARMS AND LEGS WOULD COME OFF... I SWUNG MY SWORD... ...SO HARD THAT...

...I STILL COULDN'T BEAT GIYU.

...HE HELD A REAL SWORD.

...WHEN I WENT TO FACE SABITO...

ANOTHER SIX MONTHS PASSED. UNTIL ONE DAY...

THE FIGHT WAS OVER IN AN INSTANT.

THAT DAY, IN THAT MOMENT, FOR THE FIRST TIME...

...MY BLADE REACHED SABITO FIRST.

GASP

...AND I FOUND THAT MY SWORD HAD NOT CUT SABITO'S MASK.

IT HAD SPLIT THE BOULDER.

WORDS OF GRATITUDE

Thank you to everyone who read this work and to everyone who bought it. Thanks to your support, the series will continue. I can't tell you how thankful I am. Unlike water and food, manga isn't absolutely necessary for survival. Getting you to buy it is a tough job. Thank you very much. I create this manga with the help of many people. I'll work even harder to keep it interesting for you, so please keep reading. And again... thank you!!

Sorry...

I've gotten all your letters. Thank you. They make me so happy, but I can't reply, and that makes me very sorry. Forgive me, please. I'll keep doing my best!

A DEMON'S WEAK POINT IS ITS NECK.

HOWEVER, WHEN USING A NORMAL BLADE, EVEN CUTTING ITS NECK WON'T KILL IT.

THE SWORDS THAT THE DEMON SLAYER CORPS USE ARE MADE FROM A SPECIAL STEEL.

WE CALL THEM NICHIRIN SWORDS.

CHAPTER 6: A MOUNTAIN OF HANDS

WHEN I'M FIGHTING SOME-ONE...

...AND I FIND THAT SCENT, I SEE THE THREAD.

THANK'S TO MY TRAINING WITH MAKOMO ...

...I'VE LEARNED TO SMELL OUT AN "OPENING THREAD." THAT'S HOW I WON.

GUIDED BY THE THREAD, MY BLADE CUTS INTO THAT SPOT.

IT RUNS FROM MY BLADE...

...TO A SPOT ON MY OPPONENT, AND IT GOES TAUT THE MOMENT I SEE IT.

I HAD NO WISH TO SEE ANOTHER CHILD DIE.

I DIDN'T THINK YOU WOULD SPLIT THAT BOULDER...

I DID NOT INTEND TO SEND YOU TO FINAL SELECTION.

...BUT YOU DID WELL.

...ARE AN AMAZING CHILD.

TANJIRO...

...YOU...

...BUT BE SURE TO RETURN ALIVE.

GO TO FINAL SELECTION...

YOUR SISTER AND I ARE HERE WAITING.

IT'S CALLED A WARDING MASK.

AFTER CUTTING MY HAIR...

APPARENTLY, IT OFFERS PROTECTION FROM EVIL.

UROKODAKI GAVE ME A MASK.

SO I'M LEAVING HER IN UROKO-DAKI'S CARE.

I CAN'T TAKE NEZUKO WITH ME—SHE'S STILL ASLEEP.

I'M ON MY WAY, UROKODAKI!

GIVE MY BEST TO SABITO AND MAKOMO!

TANJIRO...

...HOW IS IT YOU...

...KNOW THE NAMES OF THOSE DECEASED CHILDREN?

MOUNT
FUJIKASANE:
SITE OF FINAL
SELECTION

WOW!

BUT WISTERIA...

...SHOULDN'T BE BLOOMING THIS TIME OF YEAR.

LOOK HOW MANY THERE ARE!

IF YOU DO, THEN YOU WILL HAVE PASSED FINAL SELECTION.

HOWEVER, FROM THAT POINT ON, THE WISTERIA DOES NOT BLOOM. SO THE DEMONS ROAM FREE.

NOW GO.

YOU MUST SURVIVE THERE FOR SEVEN DAYS.

WHS

H

THE ONE WHO KILLS HIM FIRST GETS TO EAT HIM!

IT'S BEEN SO LONG SINCE I TASTED HUMAN FLESH!

WATER BREATHING!

TOTAL CONCEN-TRATION

...

I'VE GOTTEN STRONGER.

I BEAT TWO DEMONS!

DID IT.

ALL THAT TRAINING WORKED...

...I CAN DO THIS!

REST IN PEACE!

...EVEN THE BONES CRUMBLE!

WHEN I USE THE KATANA THAT URO-KODAKI GAVE ME...

KR RK SH

WHAT'S THAT ROTTEN SMELL?

UGH!

SNIFF

WAAAH!

WHSH

THERE'S A HUGE, DEFORMED DEMON BACK THERE!

I'VE NEVER SEEN ANYTHING LIKE IT!

THMP

...FOXES HAS COME!

ANOTHER OF MY DEAR...

GLARE

CHAPTER 7: SPIRITS OF THE DECEASED

DO YOU THINK...

...TANJIRO CAN REALLY DO IT?

SABITO ...?

AND YOU KNOW THAT...

...RIGHT?

...NO AMOUNT OF EFFORT IS TOO MUCH.

BUT...

I DON'T KNOW.

WOOOE

DAMN UROKO-DAKI!

DAMN UROKO-DAKI!

DAMN UROKO-DAKI!

DAMN HIM!

BRBL

BLRB

GAAAGH!

...

AGAIN AND AGAIN!

UNFOR-GIVABLE! UNFOR-GIVABLE!

ALL WHILE I'VE BEEN TRAPPED HERE!

IT'S BEEN 47 TORTUROUS YEARS!

OH, I KNOW HIM! UROKODAKI WAS THE ONE WHO CAPTURED ME! I WILL NEVER FORGET!

YOU KNOW URO—

IN THE EDO PERIOD... THE KEIO ERA!

BACK THEN HE WAS STILL A DEMON SLAYER!

NO DEMON HERE HAS BEEN ALIVE THAT LONG!

LIES!

YOU'RE LYING!

DEMON HUNTER... 'EDO PERIOD?!

...AND THEY GET KILLED DURING SELECTION!

PLUS, THE DEMONS EAT EACH OTHER TOO!

THEY ONLY PUT DEMONS UP HERE THAT HAVE EATEN TWO OR THREE PEOPLE...

...I HAVE EATEN 50 OF YOU BRATS!

BUT I HAVE SURVIVED A VERY LONG TIME. IN THIS PRISON...

...OF WISTERIA BLOSSOMS...

...A DEMON'S STRENGTH COMES FROM THE NUMBER OF PEOPLE IT HAS CONSUMED.

REMEMBER...

FIFTY?!

...AND SOME PHYSICALLY CHANGE, GAINING UNNATURAL POWERS.

THAT'S RIGHT. THEY GROW STRONGER...

IF IT EATS MANY PEOPLE IT GETS STRONGER?

...HOW MANY PEOPLE A DEMON HAS EATEN.

IF YOUR NOSE GETS STRONGER YOU'LL BE ABLE TO TELL...

?!

WHAT ARE YOU TALKING ABOUT?

...YOU ARE NUMBER 14.

...12...

...13...

...AND...

I'VE DECIDED TO KILL *ALL* OF HIS STUDENTS!

THAT'S HOW MANY OF *UROKODAKI'S STUDENTS* I HAVE EATEN!

HEE HEE

HEE

HEE HEE

HEE

THE OTHER WAS A GIRL-BRAT WHOSE KIMONO WAS COVERED IN FLOWERS.

SHE WAS SMALL AND NOT SO STRONG...

...BUT SHE WAS VERY AGILE.

HE HAD A COLORFUL JACKET, AND WAS THE STRONGEST BY FAR.

HE HAD PEACH-COLORED HAIR AND A SCAR BY HIS MOUTH.

THIRTEEN OF URO-KADAKI'S STUDENTS, BUT ABOVE ALL...

YES, INDEED!

...TWO OF THEM...

...I'LL NEVER FORGET.

HOW COULD THIS DEMON HAVE KILLED THEM? THEY TRAINED ME!

I KNOW THE GRAIN OF THOSE MASKS THAT UROKODAKI CARVES.

THEY'RE CARVED THE SAME WAY AS THE TENGU MASK HE WORE.

I RECOGNIZE YOU...

...BY THOSE FOX MASKS.

THEY'RE ALL INSIDE MY STOMACH.

IT'S LIKE UROKODAKI FED THEM TO ME!

HFF

HFF

HFF

DID HE CALL IT A "WARDING MASK"?

I ATE THEM ALL *BECAUSE* OF THE MASKS THEY WORE.

THE GIRL-BRAT WEPT AND GREW ANGRY WHEN I TOLD HER THAT.

HEH HEH HEH HEH...

HEH HEH...

HEH HEH HEH HEH...

...HE CAN'T DODGE THIS ATTACK!

GWOAH

WHUNK

THE FOX-
BRAT
IS IN
STRIKING
RANGE!

I CAN'T
GROW
MORE IN
TIME!

AND I'M
OUT OF
HANDS!

HE
ESCAPED!

WATER
BREATHING!

TOTAL
CONCENTRA-
TION.

EVEN THE
PEACH-
HAIR
COULDN'T
CUT IT!

BUT MY
NECK IS
HARD AND
IMPERVI-
OUS!

SNIFF

...AND
CRUSH IT,
JUST LIKE
I DID TO
THE OTHER
ONE!

WHEN HE
FAILS TO
CUT MY
NECK, I'LL
GRAB HIS
HEAD...

VOLUME 1 — CRUELTY (THE END)

YOU'RE READING THE
WRONG WAY!

DEMON SLAYER: KIMETSU NO YAIBA
reads from right to left, starting in the
upper-right corner. Japanese is read from
right to left, meaning that action, sound
effects and word-balloon order are completely reversed from English order.